Peter's Problem

STARTER

Alison Chaplin

AUTHOR
Alison Chaplin

EDITOR
Roanne Davis

ASSISTANT EDITOR
Dulcie Booth

SERIES DESIGNERS
Anna Oliwa/Heather Sanneh

DESIGNER
Paul Cheshire

ILLUSTRATIONS
Woody

COVER ARTWORK
Woody

Text © 2001 Alison Chaplin
© 2001 Scholastic Ltd

Designed using Adobe Pagemaker

Published by Scholastic Ltd,
Villiers House,
Clarendon Avenue,
Leamington Spa,
Warwickshire CV32 5PR

Printed by Unwin Brothers Ltd, Woking

1 2 3 4 5 6 7 8 9 0   1 2 3 4 5 6 7 8 9 0

British Library Cataloguing-in-Publication Data A catalogue record for this book is available from the British Library.

ISBN 0-439-01768-8

ACKNOWLEDGEMENTS

First performed in Manchester by participants on the 'Drama and Theatre Workshop' in August 1997. Many thanks to them for their suggestions of script changes and enthusiastic performances! Special thanks to Maggie Chaplin for her valuable assistance.

For permission to give a performance of this play at which an admission charge is made, please contact the Editorial Department, Educational Books, Scholastic Limited, Villiers House, Clarendon Avenue, Leamington Spa, Warks., CV32 5PR. You do not need to seek permission if you do not charge an entry fee for the performance. Performing licences must be applied for prior to beginning rehearsals.

Fees are £10.00 per performance for a paying audience of up to 200 people and £15.00 per performance for paying audiences of 200 people or over.

Alison Chaplin is the drama consultant for the Borough of Stockport and manager of 'Arts on the Move', a company specialising in providing a range of drama and theatre services. For information call 0161 881 0868 or visit www.artsonthemove.co.uk.

CONTENTS LIST

Peter's
Problem

INTRODUCTION

USING THIS BOOK

The aim of each performance play is to provide teachers with the necessary resources to read, rehearse and perform short plays. This book enables teachers and children to understand the process of interpreting scripts and the approaches needed for successful rehearsals and performances. From providing pre-rehearsal support to supplying linking reading and writing tasks, the contents are structured in a way that assumes no prior knowledge of script work and no previous experience of staging performances, leading those involved through the process in easy-to-follow stages.

WORKSHOP SESSIONS

These are provided to help teachers to introduce the children to the concept of drama. The sessions help the children to:

● read and understand playscripts
● explore the implicit themes and issues within the play
● appreciate character development
● learn the relevant skills required for performance.

Each session is structured to approach a different aspect of working with playscripts, using methods which are both practical and enjoyable.

PLAYSCRIPT

The playscript is organised in an easy-to-follow format, complete with full stage directions and scene changes. At the beginning of the script, following the cast list, is a brief outline of each character which provides an indication of behavioural traits and helps children to understand how that role should be performed. Most of the plays in this series are very simple to stage and require little in the way of make-up, costume or setting.

PRODUCTION SUPPORT

These notes provide practical advice to support you from the beginning to the end of the performance process, including holding auditions, structuring rehearsals, ideas for simple and effective staging, props, costumes and make-up and presenting curtain calls.

The ideas and suggestions have arisen from the author's own experience of directing the play and have, therefore, been generated by a knowledge of what has worked in practice. However, they are not prescriptive and if you feel you have the resources, time and skills to create more elaborate staging and costumes, or to approach the performance in a different way, you should feel free to do so!

LITERACY SUPPORT

The section at the end of the book is directly linked to the requirements of the National Literacy Strategy *Framework for Teaching* and provides suggestions for supportive tasks organised under the headings 'Story', 'Characters', 'Theme', 'Working with playscript layout' and 'Performance-related tasks'. Again, these are not prescriptive but aim to provide teachers with examples of how the playscript can be used to generate structured literacy work.

A FLEXIBLE RESOURCE

The unique aspect of these performance plays is that their contents can be utilised in any number of ways: as a simple reading resource; to provide a basis for literacy tasks; to introduce children to the concept of performance drama; or to produce a full-scale school production – and readers should feel free to employ the contents in any way that meets their needs. However, the most important approach for anyone using this book is to be flexible, enthusiastic and prepared to 'have a go'!

GUIDANCE FOR WORKING WITH SCRIPTS

If the children haven't had any previous experience of script work, it would be a good idea to lead them through the following simple drama process to make them familiar with the concept and style of scripted performance.

Ask the children to find a partner and then to hold a conversation together. This could be about anything – the television programmes they watched or games they played the night before, their favourite books, what they did during the school holidays, and so on.

Allow these conversations to run for about a minute, then ask the children to stop talking. Now ask the pairs to label themselves 'A' and 'B'. Tell them that they must hold a conversation again, but this time 'B' cannot respond until 'A' has finished talking (or until 'A' has finished a sentence, if 'A' is going on for too long). Insist that the children keep to this method of speaking and responding, as this forms the basis for most scripted formats.

Let these structured conversations run for about a minute and then ask the children to stop talking.

Invite them to give you feedback on the type of conversations they had and, on the board, write their statements and responses in the form of an 'A said' and 'B said' structure:

A said: …
B said: …

Record a couple of lines from each conversation, to show the children how these conversations can be recorded. Ask them to suggest how their second conversation was different from their first one. Answers should include: they had names ('A' and 'B'); they could only speak when the other person had finished speaking; the conversations were not as natural; they had to think more about what they said and how they responded to their partners.

Now ask the children to join with another pair to make a four. (Odd numbers or unequal groups are also acceptable.) Ask them to hold an initial unstructured conversation with each other about a subject of your choosing, and leave these to run for about a minute. Then ask the children to label themselves 'A', 'B', 'C' and 'D' (if there are four in the group) and to hold another conversation, this time with the same restriction imposed as before – others cannot speak until another person has finished talking. Tell the children that they do not necessarily have to join in the conversation in alphabetical order.

Invite feedback from the children about these conversations. Again, ask for suggestions about how the second discussion differed from the first and, again, record part of a structured conversation on the board, using 'A', 'B', 'C' and 'D' to indicate who speaks which lines.

Inform the children that this is how plays are structured: they are written records of people speaking to each other, having conversations or discussions, and the name of the character speaking is indicated at the beginning of each line of dialogue.

Provide the children with more practice, if necessary, by asking them to:

● record their own conversations in scripted form, for example using the 'A' and 'B' or 'A', 'B', 'C', 'D' format
● devise original conversations, using the 'A' and 'B' or 'A', 'B', 'C', 'D' format
● lift sections of dialogue from familiar stories and record them in scripted form
● rewrite their own conversations, using names instead of letters of the alphabet
● improvise a specific scene (such as someone buying an item in a shop), recording it using a tape recorder or Dictaphone, then replaying the recording to transpose it into a written script.

The main aim is to help the children appreciate that scripted text is simply dialogue, conversations or verbal statements written down, and that the format gives a clear indication of who is speaking at any one time. Tell the children that characters may interrupt each other, but that two people will never talk at the same time during a scripted performance – lines will always be spoken in sequence. Ensure they understand that playscripts, contrary to other forms of written speech, do not contain speech marks or quotation marks because the whole text is known and understood to be speech and they are therefore unnecessary.

Follow this exercise with reading and discussing an extract from any playscript, exploring how the text indicates who is speaking, analysing the sequencing of the speech and reaffirming the concept of characters speaking in turn.

As a final note, when reading the playscript in this book, ask the children to suggest what the purpose of the words in brackets or italic may be. Their answers should include: 'how characters say things', 'what characters do' and 'how characters do things'. Keep the language as simple as this initially, developing their vocabulary gradually as they become familiar with reading and understanding scripts.

THEMES AND ISSUES IN THE PLAY

Peter's Problem focuses on the difficulties faced by the central character who is being bullied because he is different from other children. Although the differences are not great, the link can be made to forms of exclusion for a wide variety of reasons.

This theme can easily be linked to PSHE objectives, allowing children the opportunity to discuss and explore the subject of bullying by responding to such questions as:

- Why do people bully?
- Why are people bullied?
- Do bullies 'work' alone or in groups? Why do you think this is?
- What can individuals do to prevent themselves from being a target for bullies?
- What can they do if they are being bullied?

These discussions will probably contain specific examples from the children's own experiences and could even lead to devising a whole-school approach to tackling and preventing bullying.

Although the play appears to have a rather indefinite conclusion, the ending provides a variety of options for Peter to use in his attempt to stop further victimisation. This reflects the different options open to children, as each individual will have a preferred way of resolving their problem. Again, discussions could explore the merits of these different options and children could make an appropriate selection or suggest an alternative.

Including animals as Peter's advisors creates a somewhat unrealistic, magical setting for the serious context and should encourage children to explore the issue of bullying without feeling threatened by what they might reveal.

Although *Peter's Problem* deals with a serious issue, the setting of the play with its fairy tale animal characters also provides an opportunity to explore the natural world – the animals' behavioural traits, habitats and so on. This should link well with any projects on nature or animal homes.

Peter's Problem is an upbeat, moralistic and gentle play which poses no threat to its young actors; but the contents and context of the play can provide a stimulus for exploring other subjects and a platform to develop the children's self-awareness.

WORKSHOP SESSIONS

These sessions should take place prior to any rehearsals or practical application of the playscript. They introduce the children to drama and theatre, develop their speaking and listening skills, generate positive group interaction, increase their levels of concentration, help to prepare them for the types of activity they will be doing during work on the playscript and develop their ability to perform confidently and effectively.

SESSION 1:
INTRODUCTORY WARM-UP

Timing: Spend up to 15 minutes on each individual activity. The whole session should take no more than 45 minutes.

Resources: A large space (such as the school hall), a card for each child of an animal name from a family group (for example Daddy duck, Mummy duck and Baby duck, including more than one baby as necessary to fit the number of children), a whistle.

Objectives: To introduce the children to the concept of drama, promote positive group interaction and encourage them to respond appropriately to instructions.

UP, DOWN, FREEZE
A WARM-UP REQUIRING CONCENTRATION AND PHYSICAL CONTROL

Explain to the children that you are going to ask them to walk around the room carefully and slowly, and that you will then call out one of several commands to which they must respond. Stress that, when they hear your command, they are to respond immediately and correctly. Anyone responding slowly or incorrectly will be 'out' and should be asked to sit aside.

Advise the children of the commands and appropriate responses:

Up: Stand with arms stretched into the air.
Down: Crouch down.
Freeze: Stand absolutely still and silent.
One leg: Stand still on one leg.
Head: Stand with hands on head.
Shoulders: Stand with hands on shoulders.
Turn: Turn and face in the opposite direction.
Go: Begin walking around the room carefully again.

Ask the children to walk around the room. Select commands according to the age and ability level of the class. Name the children who are 'out' during each turn.

Continue until you have a winner or winners and then move on to…

ANIMAL FAMILIES
INTRODUCES ROLE-PLAYING AND VOCAL SKILLS

Distribute one of the animal family cards to each child and ask the children to stand in a space.

Explain that you want them to form family groups of the animals written on the cards and to do this by performing the sound and actions of their animals. Tell the children that they cannot talk to each other to find their animal families, only locate other family members through sound and action. Advise the children that the winners will be the first group to form a complete and correct animal family.

When all of the children understand what is expected of them, instruct them to find their animal families.

Allow the activity to continue until the first complete and correct animal family group is formed, then blow your whistle, or tell the children to stop looking. Repeat this up to four times, redistributing the animal family cards each time, then thank the children for their work and move on to…

ANIMAL FREEZES

PROMOTES GROUP INTERACTION THROUGH PHYSICAL CREATIVITY

Ask the children to walk around the room carefully, without bumping into each other and to listen for you blowing your whistle. After a short time, blow the whistle, call out a number and tell the children to form a group of that number as quickly as they can. (You may wish to choose a group size that divides the class equally.)

When they are in their groups, call out the name of an animal, for example a giraffe, and tell the children that you want them to make the shape of that animal with their bodies, using everyone in their group to create the shape. (The animal could be a tortoise, rabbit, snake, eagle, elephant and so on, but all the groups should make the same animal shape that you choose.)

Count down from 10 whilst the children prepare their shapes and, after the count of 1, shout *Freeze!* Insist on stillness and silence.

Go around looking at all of the animal shapes, commenting positively on them, praising in particular those groups who have created realistic freezes. If you have time, invite the groups to view each other's freezes

Tell the children to relax and to begin walking around the room carefully again. Repeat the exercise, blowing the whistle, calling out another number and a different animal for the freezes. Remember to view and praise effective freezes each time.

When you have repeated the process with at least four different animals, thank the children for their efforts, ask them to sit in a circle with you again and end with…

CIRCLE

CHILDREN REFLECT ON AND EVALUATE THEIR SKILLS

Ask the children whether or not they enjoyed the drama session. Encourage them to give their opinions and reasons. What do they think they have learned and achieved from it? What did they enjoy the most or the least and why?

This will give you an indication of any skills and knowledge gained and can be used as a basis for developing children's abilities during additional workshop sessions.

SESSION 2:
APPROACHING THE TEXT

Timing: Spend up to 15 minutes on each activity. The whole session should take no more than 60 minutes.

Resources: One copy per child of the playscript on photocopiable pages 15–44, script extracts prepared for small group reading, board or flip chart, A3 paper, paper or work books; writing materials.

Objective: To familiarise children with the play text.

SHARED TEXT WORK

WHOLE-CLASS READING OF THE SCRIPT

Sit with the children in a circle, or with them in their classroom places. Distribute a copy of the playscript to each child and retain one yourself.

If applicable, remind the children of the drama exercise they undertook on understanding scripts (see 'Guidance for working with scripts' on page 5). Tell them that they are all going to read a play called *Peter's Problem*. Inform them that, at first, you will read the lines spoken by all of the characters, but that later you will invite some of them to read some of the lines spoken by the characters.

Ask the children to follow the words in the script as you read. (Read the lines only, do not mention who is speaking nor read the stage directions aloud.)

After reading the first section of the script yourself, ask for volunteers to read some of the other characters' lines. A good moment for this could be when PETER enters the forest (Scene 4). The children could read the lines of RABBIT 2, RABBIT 4, RAT 2, RAT 3, WOLF 2, WOLF 4, BIRD 1, BIRD 3, FOX 2 and DOZY DAFFODIL. Later, one or two children should be selected to read the lines for PETER during Scene 8 when he meets the WISE OLD OWL.

Read through the script scene by scene in this manner (stopping after each scene), combining your reading with that of volunteers (or nominees). Change readers regularly, allowing as many children as possible the opportunity to read. At the end of each section of reading, praise the children for their efforts.

When the play has been read through, thank the readers and ask all of the children to turn to the first page of the script again. Move on to…

FOCUSED WORD WORK

EXPLORING THE LANGUAGE USED IN THE PLAYSCRIPT

Invite the children to suggest words from the text that they have difficulty in understanding. Specify that these must be words that they have never seen or heard before. Write these words on the board or flip chart, working through the script quickly and recording as many of the children's suggestions as possible.

Use any remaining time to provide definitions of these words. This can be achieved in a number of different ways:

● by the children looking the words up in the dictionary, working individually with teacher guidance
● by the children working in small groups, being allocated three or four words per group, and looking these up in the dictionary
● by the teacher providing the definitions of the words on the board
● by the teacher providing the definitions of some of the words on the board, but asking children to find the definitions of others.

The process of defining words can be made more interesting by creating teams and allocating a team point each time a word is defined correctly.

Ensure that the words and their definitions are recorded on paper, in spelling books or in writing books. Leave any words not defined for further work at a later time, and move on to…

GROUP WORK

ADDITIONAL SMALL GROUP READING OF THE PLAYSCRIPT

Form the children into six small groups as suggested below, preferably of mixed reading ability. Ensure that each child retains their playscript.

Tell the children that you are going to ask each group to read a short section of the play aloud. Explain that they will be expected to read all of the lines spoken by the different characters in their allocated sections, and that this may mean some children reading the lines for more than one character. Advise the children to negotiate and distribute the character parts fairly, ensuring that each person in the group reads at least once.

Allocate each group a section of the play as follows (or using extracts of your choice):

● Group 1 (three to six children): Scene 2.
● Group 2 (five children): Scene 4.
● Group 3 (five children): Scene 5.
● Group 4 (five children): Scene 6.
● Group 5 (five children): Scene 7, from the beginning up to the BIRDS' exit.
● Group 6 (six children): Scene 7, from PETER talking to himself after the BIRDS' exit to the end of the scene.

Peter's Problem

Move from group to group, allocating the extracts and ensuring that parts have been fairly distributed. Then ask the children to begin their play readings.

Move around the room, monitoring the readings and assisting where necessary. Allow sufficient time for all readings to be completed, if possible. If you have time, ask each group in sequence to read their play section aloud to the rest of the class.

Thank the children for their efforts, ask them to stop reading and face the board again, and move on to…

STORY OUTLINE

WHOLE CLASS REVIEWING AND CONSOLIDATING KNOWLEDGE GAINED

Attach a sheet of A3 paper to the board. Write the heading *Peter's Problem* on it. Invite the children to recall the story told in the playscript, asking them to suggest sentences that provide a sequential outline of the events.

Guide their observations by asking, *What is the first important thing that happens in the play?* Record their answer on the A3 paper. Follow this by asking, *And what is the next important thing that happens?*

Continue in this fashion until you have the complete story of the events of the play written on the A3 paper in sequential outline form. Take a final moment to confirm with the children that you have recorded all of the important elements of the story.

Thank the children for their contributions and retain the A3 paper for use in the following session.

SESSION 3:
EXPLORING THE STORYLINE

Timing: Spend up to 15 minutes on each activity. The whole session should take no more than 60 minutes.

Resources: A large space (such as the school hall), the A3 sheet from the previous session, chairs (optional), tape recorder or Dictaphone (optional), copies of the playscript for reference.

Objectives: To consolidate the children's knowledge of the play contents and develop drama skills.

WHO'S TELLING THE STORY?
DEVELOPS LISTENING SKILLS AND STORYLINE KNOWLEDGE

Ask the children to lie down and close their eyes.

Explain that you are going to tap one of them on the shoulder and that, when tapped, that child must begin telling the story of what happens in *Peter's Problem*. Advise the other children to listen very carefully to both the voice and the section of the story being told. Explain that, after a short while, you will tap the child again, signalling them to stop speaking, then invite the other children to identify the speaker.

When correctly identified, select a different child to continue telling the story from the point at which the previous speaker finished. Again, this child should be asked to stop speaking and the other children asked to identify him or her. All children must keep their eyes closed at all times!

This process should be repeated until the whole story of the play has been told in this manner. Then thank the children for their efforts, ask them to open their eyes and sit up, and move on to…

STORYLINE FREEZES
PROVIDES A FOCUS FOR STORYLINE RECALL

Sit with the children in a circle. Invite the children to recall the story outline of the play that they created in the previous session. Go through the stages of the story on the A3 sheet to confirm their recollections. Explain that now they are going to create freezes that represent the story outline.

Organise the children into groups of five to eight and ask each group to find a space to work in. Instruct the children to work in their groups to make a frozen picture representing the first sentence of the play outline on the sheet. All groups should create their own freeze interpretation of the same outline sentence. Explain that these freezes should be 'as if someone had taken a photograph'.

Allow the children up to 1 minute to create their group freezes, reminding them of the setting and characters involved as they work. When this time limit has elapsed, give a countdown from 5 and after the count of 1, instruct the children to freeze. View each freeze, commenting positively on their composition, realism and effectiveness.

Repeat the process with additional sentences from the play outline, selecting as many or as few as you wish, asking the children to create a freeze picture that represents the sentence and giving the countdown each time.

Continue viewing and commenting positively on each freeze until the children have illustrated the outline of the whole play in freezes. Thank the children for their efforts, praise their work and move on to…

SOUND PICTURES

EXPLORES PLAY SETTINGS AND DEVELOPS IMAGINATIVE RESPONSES TO THE STORYLINE

Sit with the children in a circle. Lead a discussion with them about the different places (settings) connected with the play, for example the school playground; the classroom, the different areas of the forest. Go on to invite the children to suggest what sounds could be associated with these different settings, such as children playing together, children working together, the rats scurrying about next to the stream, the birds twittering and so on. Work through as many different settings from the play as possible, discussing, selecting and recording (as appropriate) sounds that could represent each one.

Then organise the children into groups of four to six. Allocate each group a different setting and ask them to devise sounds to represent that location. Explain that they should be as imaginative as possible in creating their sound pictures, not just relying on words, but using their voices, bodies and, if appropriate, objects in the room to devise interesting sound combinations. Allow the children up to 5 minutes to discuss and create their sound pictures. Move swiftly from group to group, providing assistance and advice where necessary.

When the allocated time has elapsed, ask each group to perform their sound pictures, sequencing them in order according to the playscript. Ask the groups watching to remain silent whilst others are performing their sound pictures and, at the end of each performance invite the 'audience' to applaud. Lead a brief discussion about how effective, realistic and imaginative the sounds were and whether any others could have been included. These sound pictures could then be performed as an accompaniment to

some of the storyline freezes created during the previous activity.

Finally, thank the children for their efforts, praise their work, ask them to sit in a circle with you again, and end with…

CIRCLE

CHILDREN REFLECT ON AND EVALUATE THEIR SKILLS AND KNOWLEDGE

Ask the children if they enjoyed the drama session. Invite them to give opinions and reasons for their responses. What do they think they have learned and achieved from it? What do they feel they have done well or could have done better? How do they think the activities could help them when they are performing? Ask them to suggest any additional knowledge they have gained about the storyline.

The answers will give you an indication of the skills and knowledge developed and can be used as a basis for extending the children's abilities during additional workshop sessions.

SESSION 4:
CHARACTERISATION AND ROLE-PLAY

Timing: Spend up to 20 minutes on each activity. The whole session should take no more than 60 minutes.

Resources: A large space (such as the school hall), chairs (optional), a whistle, prepared character names.

Objectives: To explore the characters in the play and encourage appropriate use of movement and language for role-play.

WALKABOUT IN ROLE

DEVELOPS CHARACTER MOVEMENT

Ask the children to walk around the room carefully. Tell them to listen for you calling out the name of one of the characters from the play, advising them to move around in silence in order to hear. Explain that, when they hear the character's name that you shout, they are to continue moving around the room, but in the style and manner of that character.

Call out the name of a character, for example Frankie, and instruct the children to *walk about as Frankie*. Observe the children as they walk about in role, commenting positively on realistic, expressive or imaginative movements. After a few seconds, ask the children to walk about as themselves again. Then repeat the 'walk about' instruction, selecting a different character from the play. Again, praise children moving in a realistic or expressive manner.

Continue until the children have walked around the room in the manner of four or five different characters from the play. Then tell the children to stop walking, thank them for their work, ask them to stand in a space, and move on to...

MOOD FREEZES

INTRODUCES DRAMATIC EXPRESSION

Ask the children to walk around the room carefully again. Advise them that this time they must listen for you blowing your whistle and should then be still and quiet. Explain that you will then call out a mood or emotion (one that might be felt by a character from the play) and they should then freeze instantly in the position of someone experiencing that mood or emotion. Examples of emotions could include fear, loneliness, excitement, anger, happiness, sadness, and so on, and all the children should perform a freeze expressing the same emotion. Remind the children that the 'freeze' command means that they should be completely still and silent.

When everyone understands what to do, blow your whistle and call out your selected mood or emotion, saying *Freeze as somebody feeling...* Ask the children to hold their frozen positions whilst you walk around the room commenting positively on those who have created realistic, expressive or imaginative freezes. Then ask the children to relax and to continue walking around the room carefully again.

Repeat the exercise, blowing your whistle and calling out a different feeling; praise effective freezes each time. Continue until the children have created at least five different freezes, then thank them for their efforts, and move quickly on to...

MOOD CONVERSATIONS

DEVELOPS EXPRESSIVE VERBAL SKILLS

Ask the children to find a partner and a space to work in (in groups with an odd number, include one group of three). Explain that they are now going to improvise (act out) conversations where people are experiencing certain moods or emotions.

Tell the children that they are going to hold a simple conversation with their partners about, for example, where they went on holiday (or what they watched on television yesterday, their favourite food, what they like about school – the choice is up to you but everyone should hold the same conversation).

Advise the children that you will then call out a mood, or emotion and that they should then continue their conversations as if they were both experiencing that emotion.

Allow the conversations to continue normally for a few seconds and then call out a mood, for example sadness (or another feeling experienced by characters from the play), and ask the children to continue their conversations as if both of them were feeling sad.

Change the conversation subject and the feelings regularly, allowing each improvised conversation to continue for up to 30 seconds. Repeat the process until the children have improvised holding conversations expressing at least four different moods or emotions. Then stop the activity, thank and praise the children, ask them to sit in a circle with you again, and end with...

CIRCLE

CHILDREN REFLECT ON AND EVALUATE THEIR SKILLS AND KNOWLEDGE

Ask the children whether or not they enjoyed that drama session. Ask them to give reasons for their answers. What do they think they have learned and achieved from the session? What do they feel they have done well or might have done better? How do they think the activities could help them when they are performing? Ask the children to comment on what they have learned about the characters in *Peter's Problem*.

This information could be used as a basis for future workshop sessions.

SESSION 5: CONSOLIDATING PERFORMANCE SKILLS

Timing: Spend up to 20 minutes on each activity. The whole session should take no more than 60 minutes.

Resources: A large space (such as the school hall), a copy of the playscript for each child, chairs (optional), A3 paper (optional), the sequential story outline from Session 2.

Objectives: To consolidate understanding of the play and provide a focus for performance skills.

CHARACTER IMPROVISATIONS

DEVELOPS ROLE-PLAYING SKILLS

Ask the children to find a partner and a space to work in (for groups with an odd number, one pair can work as a three). Explain that you are going to ask them to consider who Peter might have talked to about being bullied and what he would have said. Invite the children to suggest ideas. These could include his parents, class teacher, headteacher, a lunchtime organiser, an aunt (or other relative) and so on. Acknowledge all responses.

Tell the children that you are going to ask them to act out some of these conversations between Peter and the people he might have spoken to. (Other ideas as suggested by the children could also be included, or used as alternatives.) Ask the children to decide in their pairs who will be Peter and who will act as the person he is talking to. Then tell everyone who that character is to be. Explain that Peter should talk about his problem and ask for advice and support from the other character, who should advise him accordingly.

Allow the children up to 30 seconds to allocate roles, plan and discuss their improvisations and then ask them to begin. Move quickly around the room, listening to as many improvised conversations as you can and praising those children who are working and responding in role effectively. After about 1 minute, ask the children to swap roles and repeat the improvised scene.

Tell the children to find a new partner and ask them to improvise (act out) Peter talking to a different person. Again, allow only a few seconds for discussion and negotiation of roles. After a minute of performance, ask the children to swap roles again and to continue their new conversation. Move around the room again, listening to the children's improvisations and praising any expressive or considered performances.

Continue repeating the activity until the children have improvised a number of different situations involving Peter, then lead a brief discussion, inviting children to feed back what 'Peter' said and what advice he was given.

Finally, thank the children for their work, comment positively on their efforts, and move quickly on to…

STORYLINE IMPROVISATIONS

CONSOLIDATES TEXT KNOWLEDGE AND PERFORMANCE SKILLS

Organise the children into groups of six to eight and display the story outline sheet from Session 2 as a reference. Tell the children that you would like them to work in their groups to perform the whole story of the play, *Peter's Problem*, acting it out in their own words.

Advise the children to agree amongst themselves who will play the different parts, but not to worry about having enough people to act out all of the characters. Explain that it is more important to show what happens in the story. Let them know that their performances must not last more than 3 minutes and that when they have practised their mini-plays, they will be able to show them to each other. Give the groups up to 5 minutes to plan and rehearse their mini-plays, moving quickly from group to group to ensure that children are working fairly and productively.

When the rehearsal time is up, ask each group to show their performance in turn. Encourage the children observing as an audience to applaud after each performance. When each performance has been seen, thank the children for their work, praise their efforts. Then move quickly on to...

SCRIPT EXTRACTS

REINTRODUCES THE PLAYSCRIPT AND PREPARES CHILDREN FOR PERFORMANCE

Tell the children that you are going to ask them to act out sections of the script to each other. Explain that their performances can either be simple readings, or include actions and movement as well.

Distribute copies of the script, retaining one for yourself. Organise the children into groups of appropriate numbers (ideally of mixed reading ability) and allocate script extracts for performance, for example:

- Group 1 (five to eight) children: Scene 1.
- Group 2 (five to eight children): Scene 3.
- Group 3 (three to five children): Scene 4.
- Group 4 (three to five children): Scene 5.
- Group 5 (three to five children): Scene 6.
- Group 6 (three to five children): Scene 7, from the beginning up to the BIRDS' exit.
- Group 7 (three to five children): Scene 7, from PETER talking to himself after the BIRDS' exit to the end of the scene.
- Group 8 (three to five children): Scene 8.

Advise the children that some of them may have to speak the lines for more than one character. The aim is to encourage them to learn how to read, prepare and perform the script. Performances can be static or involve movement but, in either case, children should be encouraged to use vocal and facial expression.

Allow the children up to 8 minutes to read and rehearse their script extracts. Move from group to group, ensuring that parts have been distributed fairly and that everyone is working productively.

When the rehearsal time has elapsed, ask each group to show their performances, or read their extracts, in sequence. Invite those observing as audience members to remain silent during each performance and to applaud after it. When all the groups have acted out their extracts, thank the children for their work, praise their efforts, ask them to sit in a circle with you, and end with...

CIRCLE

CHILDREN REFLECT ON AND EVALUATE THEIR SKILLS AND KNOWLEDGE

Ask the children if they enjoyed the drama session. Invite their opinions and reasons. Ask them which aspect they enjoyed the most and the least, and why. What do they think they have learned or achieved from the activities? What do they feel is the most important skill they have learned? What do they feel they have done well? Could they have done some things better? How do they feel about their performances? What would they change if they had the chance to perform again? What do they feel is the most important thing to remember when performing in front of others? (If you wish, record their answers on A3 paper to provide a visual prompt during rehearsals.) Acknowledge all the children's responses, thank them for all their hard work and praise their efforts.

Peter's Problem

CAST LIST

Peter	Rat 3
Frankie	Rat 4
Billy	Wolf 1
Tommy	Wolf 2
Lenny	Wolf 3
Jenny	Wolf 4
Sally	Bird 1
Lucy	Bird 2
Claire	Bird 3
Mrs Moore	Bird 4
Rabbit 1	Fox 1
Rabbit 2	Fox 2
Rabbit 3	Daft Daffodil
Rabbit 4	Dozy Daffodil
Rat 1	Dynamic Daffodil
Rat 2	Wise Old Owl

32 characters (additional children may be included as animals in non-speaking roles).

SCENES

1 The school playground
2 The classroom
3 The school playground, later that day
4 The forest
5 Down by the stream
6 Near the wolves' den
7 By the oak trees
8 At the elm tree
9 School, a few days later

Photocopiable

CHARACTER OUTLINES

PETER: Hardworking and kind. Enjoys drama, music, reading – and school!

FRANKIE: Nasty. Likes tormenting Peter. Leads the other bullies.

BILLY: Cruel. Picks on Peter and always follows Frankie's lead.

TOMMY: Hates school and doesn't like feeling stupid.

LENNY: Sarcastic. Likes to make fun of everyone.

JENNY: Hates people who are clever. Likes to pick on Peter.

SALLY: Follows the other bullies, but really wants to be friends with Peter.

LUCY: Nasty. Likes to stir up as much trouble as possible and will pick on anyone.

CLAIRE: Has a very short temper and enjoys bullying Peter.

MRS MOORE: A strict but fair teacher. Concerned about Peter.

RABBIT 1: Slightly fearful, with a kind nature.

RABBIT 2: Nosy. Likes to listen to other people's problems.

RABBIT 3: Gets irritated easily and can be quite sarcastic.

RABBIT 4: Intelligent. Likes to help others.

RAT 1: The rat pack leader whom all the other rats follow.

RAT 2: Hardworking, with a good nature.

RAT 3: Hardworking. Likes being part of the pack.

RAT 4: Likes to be an individual. Irritates Rat 1.

WOLF 1: The wolf pack leader. Very strong and brave.

WOLF 2: Brave. Has a good sense of humour.

WOLF 3: Brave and likes fighting.

WOLF 4: Brave and likes to help others.

BIRD 1: Happy. Enjoys singing.

BIRD 2: Intelligent, with a positive nature.

BIRD 3: Friendly and likes to make other people happy.

BIRD 4: Sensible. Leads the bird group.

FOX 1: Unpleasant, even nasty, and not very bright.

FOX 2: Intelligent, with a sly and slightly cruel attitude.

DAFT DAFFODIL: Enjoys being helpful. Can get very excited.

DOZY DAFFODIL: Slightly sleepy. Agrees with everything the other daffodils say.

DYNAMIC DAFFODIL: Bright and cheerful and very smart.

WISE OLD OWL: A kindly and sensible character. Intelligent and helpful.

Photocopiable

Scene 1: The school playground

The BOYS and GIRLS except PETER are on stage, playing and fighting.
PETER enters slowly and cautiously.

FRANKIE: *(shouting)* It's Peter the pumpkin eater!

The CHILDREN ALL surround PETER.

JENNY: *(to PETER)* Have you done your homework?

PETER: Yes.

CLAIRE: *(annoyed)* Oh, what did you go and do that for?

PETER: Because Mrs Moore told us to.

LENNY: *(mimicking him nastily)* Because Mrs Moore told us to!

BILLY: Now we'll all get in trouble!

SALLY: *(to LUCY)* Did you do it, Lucy?

LUCY: Half of it. I couldn't do the rest.

SALLY: *(to TOMMY)* Did you do it, Tommy?

TOMMY: No. I didn't understand it.

FRANKIE: *(to EVERYONE)* Did anyone do the homework?

EVERYONE except FRANKIE and PETER shakes their head or ad-libs "No", "A bit of
it...", "It was too hard..." and so on.

LENNY: So, the only one to do it was you, Peter.

BILLY: Great! You're going to make us look really bad.

JENNY: I bet I get another telling-off.

LUCY: Yeah. We'll be kept in every break for the rest of this week.

Photocopiable

CLAIRE: Well done, Peter! Why can't you be like the rest of us?

TOMMY: Yeah. We never do our homework.

LENNY: *(to TOMMY)* You never do it, Tommy, because you never understand it.

TOMMY: Well, even if I did understand it, I still wouldn't do it!

FRANKIE snatches PETER'S school-bag from him.

FRANKIE: Well, I'm going to sort this out!

PETER: Give me that back, Frankie!

FRANKIE: *(to PETER)* Shut up, teacher's pet! You're not going to get us into trouble again.

PETER makes a dash for his bag.

FRANKIE: Catch it, Billy!

FRANKIE throws the bag to BILLY. PETER tries to get it again.

BILLY: To you, Claire. Get his homework out!

BILLY throws the bag to CLAIRE.
TOMMY and LENNY grab and hold PETER.
CLAIRE and JENNY empty the bag onto the floor.

JENNY: Look at all these books. He's a real swot. *(To PETER)* Aren't you?!

PETER: Give me that back! Leave my things alone!

LUCY: Aah! He's going to cry.

CLAIRE: *(finding the homework book)* Got it!

CLAIRE passes the homework book to FRANKIE.

FRANKIE: Well done, Claire.

FRANKIE finds the homework pages, rips them out and stuffs them in his pocket.

FRANKIE: Right! Now he hasn't done his homework, either.

FRANKIE hands the book back to CLAIRE who drops it on the floor with the rest of the bag's contents.

LENNY: We better go and check that no one else has done it.

JENNY: At least we've sorted him out.

LUCY: Mary Peterson sometimes does hers.

JENNY: Yeah, she's another teacher's pet. They ought to get together!

EVERYONE (except PETER) laughs nastily.

BILLY: Come on, then.

EVERYONE exits except PETER and SALLY who hang back.
PETER is putting everything back in his school-bag. SALLY begins to help him.

SALLY: Why do you do it, Peter?

PETER: Do what?

SALLY: Behave differently from the rest of us?

PETER: I don't.

SALLY: Yes, you do. You're always reading, always doing your homework on time and you never play football with the others.

PETER: I don't like football.

SALLY: That's what I mean. Couldn't you just pretend?

PETER: I'm just not interested in it, Sally.

SALLY: Well, what are you interested in, then?

PETER: I like reading and listening to music and, best of all, I like doing drama.

SALLY: See what I mean? You're just asking to get picked on.

PETER: Well, I don't see why. I've not done anything to them. Why can't they just leave me alone?

SALLY: Because you're too different, Peter. They don't like people who are different.

PETER: I can't help it, can I?

SALLY: That's just it – you can help it. Try to be a bit more like them – that's my advice – unless you want to keep being bullied.

PETER: Look, they've been picking on me since the first day I came here and it's not going to change now. There's nothing I can do about it.

SALLY: Well, just think about it, that's all. *(She pauses)* I'd better go and join them or they'll think I'm on your side and start picking on me too.

SALLY exits.
PETER finishes putting away his things and then he exits.

Scene 2: The classroom

The CHILDREN are sitting in front of MRS MOORE.

MRS MOORE: *(angrily)* I can't believe that none of you have done the homework! It wasn't that difficult – we'd covered most of it during the lesson.

Photocopiable

TOMMY: *(putting his hand up)* I really tried, Mrs Moore.

MRS MOORE: I'm sure you did, Tommy, but really you're all as bad as each other. You will stay in this break time, and every break this week, until you've all caught up with the homework you should have finished. Is that understood?

ALL OF THE CHILDREN: *(in unison)* Yes, Mrs Moore.

MRS MOORE: Right. Go and get changed for PE. *(The CHILDREN all exit quickly. MRS MOORE stops PETER leaving)* Peter, could I speak to you for a moment, please?

PETER remains behind.

MRS MOORE: I'm surprised that you didn't hand your homework in. It's not like you. Is there something wrong?

There is a pause whilst PETER decides what to say.

MRS MOORE: Is something worrying you, Peter? Did you find it too difficult? *(PETER shakes his head)* Then what is it?

PETER: Well... *(Pause)* ...I did do the homework, but...

MRS MOORE: *(encouragingly)* Yes?

PETER: *(quickly)* ...but it got taken off me.

MRS MOORE: Taken off you? Who took it?

PETER responds by shrugging his shoulders. He is not prepared to give names.

MRS MOORE: Don't worry, I think I can guess. All right, Peter, leave it with me. *(She pauses as PETER hesitates)* Off you go.

PETER exits.
MRS MOORE stands thinking for a few seconds and then exits.

Photocopiable

Scene 3: The school playground, later that day

PETER enters and suddenly comes face to face with ALL of the OTHER CHILDREN who enter from the opposite side of the stage.

BILLY: You snitched on us, didn't you?

LUCY: Yeah. You told Mrs Moore that it was us who stole your homework.

PETER: *(protesting)* I didn't!

LENNY: *(disbelieving)* Oh no? Well, how come she's just gone mad at us, then?

TOMMY: And she's keeping us back after school. My dad'll go mad at me if I get into any more trouble.

PETER: I didn't tell Mrs Moore who took my homework!

FRANKIE: Well, she's suddenly become a mind-reader then because she seemed to know it was us.

CLAIRE: What did you say?

PETER: Nothing! She asked me where my homework was and I just told her that it was taken off me.

JENNY: Oh great! You've got us into real trouble.

FRANKIE: Yeah! And we're going to sort you out, Peter, so you'd better watch it!

THE OTHER CHILDREN EXCEPT PETER: *(in unison)* Yeah!

BILLY: *(menacingly)* We'll get you for this, you just wait and see!

The CHILDREN all push past PETER and exit.
PETER stands alone for a few moments and then picks up his bag with a determined look on his face.

PETER: *(to himself)* That's it, I've had enough! I'm going where no one can get me. I'll run away to the forest. *(Pause)* That'll make them sorry.

PETER exits.

SCENE 4: The forest

The RABBITS are hopping about on stage.
PETER enters, carrying a tree stump which he sits on. He watches the rabbits.

PETER: *(thinking aloud)* What am I going to do? If I go back, I'll get beaten up. I'm really fed up.

RABBIT 1: What's wrong, my friend?

PETER jumps up and looks around in surprise, wondering where the voice came from.

RABBIT 2: You look really unhappy. What's the matter?

PETER: *(looking around again)* What?! Who's that?

RABBIT 3: *(to the other RABBITS)* Is he completely daft?

RABBIT 4: *(to PETER)* Down here! It's us.

PETER: That's funny – I felt sure that those rabbits were talking to me. But that's stupid!

RABBIT 4: You're the stupid one, mate! Of course it's us talking, who did you think it was?

PETER: This is mad. Rabbits can't talk!

RABBIT 3: How do you know? Have you ever bothered to listen?

Photocopiable

PETER: You *are* talking!

RABBIT 2: Of course we *are*! *(Pause)* Now, tell us what's troubling you and why you look so unhappy.

PETER: Yeah, right! When I start telling my problems to rabbits, that's when they lock me away for good!

RABBIT 3: *(sulkily)* Oh, please yourself. We were only trying to help.

PETER: *(hesitantly)* Can you help?

RABBIT 4: Try us. We may look stupid with these daft tails and twitchy noses, but deep down we're very sensitive and intelligent, *(To the OTHER RABBITS)* aren't we?

The OTHER RABBITS nod and ad-lib their agreement, saying "Yes", "That's right", "Certainly" and so on.

PETER: Oh well, it can't do any harm I suppose. *(Pause, then slightly hurriedly)* I'm being bullied at school and today I did something that made things worse and so now I'm in even more serious trouble and they're all going to get me.

RABBIT 3: That *is* a problem. Why are they bullying you?

PETER: I don't know, really. Sally says it's because I'm different.

RABBIT 1: And are you?

PETER: Am I what?

RABBIT 1: Different.

PETER: I don't know. They seem to think so. I don't like sport and would rather do drama instead, so I suppose I am.

RABBIT 2: *(to EVERYONE)* We don't really know what it's like to be different, do we? I mean, we all have our own personalities, don't get me wrong, but we all do the same things every day.

Photocopiable

RABBIT 3:   *(nodding in agreement)* That's right. We sleep, wake up, eat, play, hop about, eat some more and then sleep again. It's quite a good life, really.

PETER: So you can't really help me deal with these bullies, then?

RABBIT 1:   Oh, we didn't say that. No, not at all. We have a foolproof way of dealing with things that threaten us.

PETER: *(excited)* Oh yes? What's that?

RABBIT 1:   *(pausing briefly)* We run away.

PETER: *(disappointed)* Oh.

RABBIT 3:   Yes, we leg it down the nearest rabbit hole. Works every time.

RABBIT 2:   We wait in our burrows until the threat has passed and then, when it's safe, we come out again.

RABBIT 4:   Until the next time something threatens us and then we just run away again – simple!

PETER: So that's your advice? I should run away and hide?

RABBIT 1:   *(nodding)* Works for us.

PETER: Yes, well, thank you, but I don't think that will help. For one thing, what if they come after me?

RABBIT 1:   *(thinking)* Hmm. Never thought of that. *(Pause)* You could take up jogging.

PETER: And for another thing…

RABBIT 3:   Yes?

PETER: …I wouldn't fit down a rabbit hole.

Photocopiable

RABBIT 3: *(looking carefully at PETER)* Oh no, you wouldn't really, would you?

PETER: So, thank you, but maybe I need to find some different advice.

RABBIT 2: *(excited)* I know who you could ask!

PETER: Who?

RABBIT 2: The rats who live by the stream. They've always got plenty to say for themselves.

PETER: *(astonished)* Rats?! Rats can talk too?

RABBIT 4: *(sighing irritatedly)* Of course they can. *(Brief pause)* Look, you've got to get over this prejudice of yours and accept that the animals in this forest speak and, for today at least, you can hear them. All right?

PETER: All right. *(Pause)* So where do I find the rats?

RABBIT 1: Down by the stream; we told you.

PETER: And where's the stream?

RABBIT 1: *(realising)* Oh, sorry. *(Nods offstage)* It's that way. Just keep walking in a straight line following the path and, when your feet get wet, you've arrived.

PETER: Right. And thank you.

RABBIT 4: You're welcome. Sorry we couldn't be more helpful.

PETER: I'll be off then. Bye.

ALL RABBITS: Bye! Good luck.

PETER exits.

Photocopiable

RABBIT 2: Right, then! Is it a game of tig or do we go down to the dandelion patch and chew a few leaves?

RABBIT 4: Well I'm a bit peckish.

RABBIT 1: Me too.

RABBIT 3: Me three.

RABBIT 2: OK, dandelion patch it is, then. Last one there's a guinea pig!

The RABBITS all exit quickly.

SCENE 5: Down by the stream

The RATS enter. They dash about, moving objects from one side of the stage and back again for no apparent reason! They take their work very seriously.
PETER enters.

PETER: *(to the RATS)* Excuse me!

The RATS stop for a second to look at PETER, then carry on working.

PETER: *(slightly louder)* Excuse me! The rabbits suggested that I come and talk to you. I have a bit of a problem, you see, and I'd really appreciate your help.

RAT 1: We're busy.

RAT 2: Busy.

RAT 3: Busy.

RAT 4: Very busy.

The RATS continue to run about as PETER tries to talk to them.

PETER: I'm sorry to disturb you. It won't take long.

RAT 1:   No time!

RAT 2:   No time!

RAT 3:   No time!

RAT 4:   No time to spare!

PETER: No, I can see that. It's just that I have this problem at school, you see. I'm being bullied and I don't know what to do about it.

The RATS all stop moving and look at PETER. The RATS then gather together and talk to each other.

RAT 1:   Bullied?

RAT 2:   Bullied?

RAT 3:   Bullied?

RAT 4:   He's being bullied.

The RATS whisper briefly amongst themselves, then begin dashing around again, giving their advice to PETER whilst they are moving.

RAT 1:   Run up their trouser legs.

RAT 2:   Run over their faces.

RAT 3:   Scurry over their feet.

RAT 4:   Scratch about in their skirting boards.

PETER: *(confused)* What?

RAT 1:   Always works for us.

RAT 2:   Works for us.

RAT 3:   Works for us.

RAT 4:   Works for me.

PETER: Well, I'm sure that it does and that's very interesting, but it's not really what I was looking for. Is there anything else you can suggest?

The RATS all stop moving briefly and consider this. Then they move about again.

RAT 1:   We must get on.

RAT 2:   Get on.

RAT 3:   Get on.

RAT 4:   Get on with our work.

PETER: Yes, I can see you're busy. I won't disturb you any more. Do you know anyone else who may be able to help me?

RAT 1:   Try the wolves.

RAT 2:   The wolves.

RAT 3:   The wolves.

RAT 4:   Over there. *(Points offstage)*

PETER: *(nervously)* Wolves? I'm not too sure about that. Well, thank you anyway. Goodbye.

RAT 1:   Goodbye.

RAT 2:   Goodbye.

RAT 3:   Goodbye.

RAT 4:   See you!

PETER exits.
The RATS begin to collect up all of the objects on stage.

Photocopiable

RAT 1: To the stream!

RAT 2: The stream.

RAT 3: The stream.

RAT 4: Everyone to the stream!

RAT 1: *(to RAT 4)* Will you stop doing that?

RAT 4: What?

RAT 1: Saying different things to the rest of us.

RAT 4: *(protesting)* I don't.

RAT 1: Yes, you do.

The RATS exit, continuing to argue. They take all of the objects offstage with them.

SCENE 6: Near the wolves' den

PETER enters, searching nervously for the wolves. He moves slowly and cautiously. Suddenly WOLF 1 jumps out in front of him, growling loudly. PETER jumps in fright.

WOLF 1: Who are you and what are you doing in this forest?

PETER: *(timidly)* I'm Peter. The rats sent me to you. I've come for some advice.

WOLF 1: Peter, eh? My grandfather knew someone called Peter. He was very famous, you know. They wrote a tune about him. *Peter and the Wolf* it was called. Perhaps you've heard of it?

PETER: *(nervously)* Er... yes. Yes, I have.

WOLF 1: Any relation to you?

PETER: Er... no. No, I don't think so.

Photocopiable

WOLF 1: Oh good. *(Grim faced)* My grandfather came to a sticky end because of him. *(Pauses)* What was it that you wanted?

PETER: *(backing away a little)* Some advice. But it doesn't really matter. I don't want to waste your time.

PETER backs away a little more, as if to exit. He is terrified.

WOLF 1: It's no problem, we have time to spare. Stay right here and I'll fetch the other members of the pack.

WOLF 1 exits.
PETER looks around and considers leaving. Just as he decides to go,
the WOLVES enter.

WOLF 2: Is this him?

WOLF 1: Yes.

WOLF 3: He's very small, isn't he?

WOLF 4: What did he say he wanted?

WOLF 1: Some advice. *(Pauses briefly)* Now, Peter, go ahead. We're all ears.

The WOLVES all fall about laughing at this 'joke' because they do all have large ears.

WOLF 2: *(wiping tears of laughter from his eyes)* Ooh! That always makes me laugh!

WOLF 3: *(trying to regain control)* Stop it, now, stop it. This poor lad wants our help. Let's be serious now.

WOLF 4: *(to PETER)* Sorry. Tell us what your problem is.

PETER: Well, I'm being bullied at school and, just recently, it's become even worse and I really don't know what to do about it. I've spoken to the rabbits, who just suggested running away…

WOLF 2:   *(derisively)* They would.

PETER: ...and I've talked to the rats, who were no use at all really...

WOLF 1:   That's no surprise.

PETER: ...but they suggested that I come and talk to you, so here I am. I must admit that this is turning into one of the strangest days I've ever had.

WOLF 3:   Bullies, eh? I've heard of them. Nasty little creatures.

PETER: Yes... no... well, sort of.

WOLF 3:   And you want us to suggest a way of dealing with them?

PETER: Yes, please.

WOLF 4:   Well, why don't you do what we always do when faced with an enemy?

PETER: And what's that?

WOLF 4:   Get ourselves into a gang and attack. It never fails.

WOLF 2:   *(nodding in agreement)* No good trying to tackle them on your own.

WOLF 1:   No. It has to be a gang of you.

WOLF 3:   And you have to fight nasty, or you'll never win.

PETER: *(doubtfully)* Fight? Attack in a gang? I don't think I'd like that. Isn't that behaving just like them?

WOLF 2:   Well, yes, of course it is.

PETER: So, what's the point?

WOLF 4:   The point? The point?! *(To the other WOLVES)* What *is* the point?

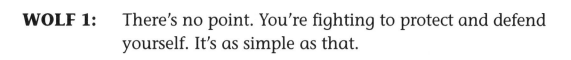

WOLF 1: There's no point. You're fighting to protect and defend yourself. It's as simple as that.

PETER: Well, thank you, but I think, if it's all the same to you, that I'll keep looking for advice. I really don't fancy getting a gang and having a battle.

WOLF 3: *(surprised)* You don't?

PETER: No, not really. *(Pause)* Is there anyone else I could ask about this?

WOLF 2: *(unsure)* Well, there's the birds over in the oak trees, they might be able to help. They certainly make enough noise all day.

WOLF 4: Yes, they're always chattering. I'm sure some of it must be sensible.

PETER: I'll go and see them then, thank you. Thanks very much for your time.

WOLF 1: You're welcome. Good luck.

PETER: Bye.

PETER exits.
The WOLVES all look at each other in amazement.

WOLF 2: Fancy him not wanting to form a pack and have a fight!

WOLF 3: I know. It just doesn't make sense, does it? Oh well, I'll never understand the youth of today.

The WOLVES all exit, chattering amongst themselves as they go.

SCENE 7: By the oak trees

The DAFFODILS enter and position themselves at the side of a tree stump, which they bring on with them.
The BIRDS enter. They are singing a modern pop song together.
PETER enters just as the BIRDS finish their song. He applauds them.

PETER: I assume you are the birds that the wolves sent me to speak to. That singing was lovely, I didn't know you sang pop tunes.

BIRD 1: Well, we do. It's just that they don't normally sound like that to you.

BIRD 2: It normally sounds like just a lot of twittering and tweeting, but we actually know lots of tunes!

BIRD 3: Did you say that the wolves sent you over to us?

PETER: Yes, for some advice.

BIRD 4: About what?

PETER: Well, the problem is that I'm getting bullied at school and I don't know what to do about it.

BIRD 1: Have you asked the other animals?

PETER: Yes. I've spoken to the rabbits, the rats and the wolves, but no one's come up with anything useful so far.

BIRD 2: And you want to know how to deal with these bullies who are making you unhappy?

PETER: *(hopefully)* Yes, please.

BIRD 4: *(looks at the other BIRDS)* Excuse us a moment, please. I think we need to discuss this.

The BIRDS have a short 'meeting', with lots of twittering and tweeting, then turn back to PETER.

BIRD 4: Well, we know what we'd do.

PETER: *(excited)* Yes? Yes?

BIRD 3: We'd pass it on.

PETER: *(confused)* Pardon?

BIRD 1: Talk about it.

BIRDS 2, 3 & 4: *(in unison)* Tell everyone.

BIRD 1: It never fails.

BIRD 4: Sing it from the rooftops.

BIRD 2: It always makes things better if you tell someone else.

BIRD 4: So, there you go. Spread the news far and wide. That should do it.

PETER: *(disappointed)* Yes, but I've already… Oh, never mind. Thank you very much, you've been most helpful.

BIRD 3: You're welcome. We always like to make people happy whenever we can.

The BIRDS exit, singing together again.
PETER sits on the tree stump feeling very dejected.

PETER: *(to himself)* I'm never going to get a sensible answer to this! I might just as well go back and face the beating and get it over with.

PETER sighs sadly and sits silently in thought.
The FOXES enter.

FOX 1: That boy's talking to himself.

FOX 2: Yes, he is, isn't he?

Photocopiable

FOX 1:   *(to FOX 2)* Sad, isn't it?

FOX 2:   Yes. *(Pause, then slyly)* But it might be to our advantage.

FOX 1:   How do you mean?

FOX 2:   *(tapping the side of his head)* Well, if he's not 'all there', we could have a bit of fun with him.

FOX 1:   *(realising)* Oh yes, so we could!

The FOXES approach PETER.

FOX 2:   *(to PETER)* Good afternoon, young man, and what brings you to this part of the forest?

PETER: *(startled)* Who…? Oh, you're foxes. I'm Peter and I've run away from a gang of bullies at my school and have been wandering through this forest, talking to different animals, trying to get some sensible advice on how to deal with them.

FOX 1:   And?

PETER: And what?

FOX 1:   And have you been given any sensible advice?

PETER: No. None at all. I was just thinking of going back to face the bullies and accept their beating.

FOX 2:   Oh, you mustn't do that!

FOX 1:   No, no, not at all!

PETER: Why not?

FOX 2:   Well, I'm sure that we can think of a cunning way to resolve your problem.

FOX 1:   Yes, there must be a clever method of dealing with this.

Photocopiable

The DAFFODILS suddenly lift their heads.

DAFT DAFFODIL: Don't listen to them!

FOX 1: *(to DAFT DAFFODIL)* Shut up, you!

DOZY DAFFODIL: Stay in the forest!

FOX 2: Mind your own business, will you? You're daffodils and daffodils can't speak.

DOZY DAFFODIL: *(sarcastically)* Oh, we can't, can we?

FOX 2: *(trying to ignore the DAFFODILS)* Anyway, as I was saying before we were so rudely interrupted, we need to approach this slyly. Have you told anyone that you're being bullied?

PETER: Like who?

FOX 2: Your parents, a teacher, the head, a family friend, anyone?

PETER: Well, no.

FOX 1: Well, why not? That's what I'd do. Go behind their backs and tell on them to everyone!

DAFT DAFFODIL: Don't listen to them!

DOZY DAFFODIL: No. Don't listen to them!

FOX 2: *(now very annoyed)* Will you stop?! Listen to me, Peter. In these sort of situations you need to be a little bit clever, a little bit sharp. Do you understand what I'm saying?

PETER: No, not really.

FOX 1: Get them into trouble. As much as you can. Tell everyone all about their behaviour. *(Pause)* Why haven't you told anyone?

PETER: Well, I haven't told my parents because I didn't want to worry them and I'm already in big trouble because of something I said to the teacher, Mrs Moore, so there's no way I'm doing that again and, anyway, I thought that if I just left it and ignored the situation, it might go away and they might leave me alone.

FOX 1: Fair enough, I suppose. I can understand that reasoning.

FOX 2: *(to FOX 1)* It's unlikely that they will just leave him alone, though, isn't it?

FOX 1: Very unlikely. I'd say that this calls for some serious thinking on our part.

DAFT DAFFODIL: Don't listen to them.

DOZY DAFFODIL: Listen to us.

FOX 2: Look! I've already told you once, Daffodils can't speak!

DYNAMIC DAFFODIL: Why doesn't he go and see the wise old owl?

FOX 1: Oh, blimey, there's another one chiming in now!

PETER: *(to DYNAMIC DAFFODIL)* I beg your pardon?

DYNAMIC DAFFODIL: Why don't you go and speak to the wise old owl? He knows the answer to everything, I'm sure he'll be able to help you.

Photocopiable

DAFT
DAFFODIL &
DOZY
DAFFODIL: *(in unison)* Yeah! Hooray for Dynamic Daffodil! Go and see the wise old owl.

PETER: Do you think so? Where does he live?

DYNAMIC
DAFFODIL: In the largest elm tree in the middle of the forest. You can't miss it.

PETER: Thanks very much for your help, daffodils, and you too foxes. I'm off to see the wise old owl.

PETER exits.

FOX 2:   *(to the DAFFODILS)* Why can't you lot just mind your own business?

FOX 1:   Yeah! We had a good thing going there until you interrupted and spoilt it.

FOX 2:   Honestly, it comes to something when you can't even have a civilised adult conversation without a load of daffodils interrupting you!

FOX 1:   You three should learn to mind your own business, otherwise you might just find yourselves de-headed one of these days!

The FOXES exit, muttering angrily to each other.
The lights fade to blackout and the DAFFODILS exit, taking the tree stump with them.

SCENE 8: At the elm tree

The WISE OLD OWL enters, carrying a rocking chair which he positions and sits down on. He begins to read a book or to complete a crossword puzzle. PETER, offstage, makes a sound like he is knocking at the door.

WISE OLD OWL: Enter!

PETER enters slowly and cautiously.

PETER: Excuse me, but are you the wise old owl?

WISE OLD OWL: *(proudly)* I am.

PETER: I'm sorry to disturb you, but I'm Peter and I really need your help and advice.

WISE OLD OWL: Come in, come in! How can I help you?

PETER: Well, I'm being bullied at school. It's been going on a long time and it's getting worse. I really don't know what to do. I don't want to tell my parents, and the teachers can't help either. I've spent all day in this forest talking to lots of different animals and they've all given me different advice, but none of it is really of any use and so I've come to see you in the hope that you can help me.

WISE OLD OWL: A very wise decision if I may say so. *(Pause)* Now, just what advice have you been given?

PETER: Well, the rabbits think I should run away, the rats told me to irritate the bullies, the wolves think I should fight back, the birds say I should tell everyone and the foxes want me to be sly and cunning.

WISE OLD
OWL: *(peering at PETER over the top of his spectacles)* Hmm. Hmm. Is it just you they bully?

PETER: No, they pick on others as well, but I seem to be the one they take the most pleasure in bullying. They steal my homework.

WISE OLD
OWL: And why do you think that is?

PETER: Well, I think it's because I'm different. I enjoy different things, like reading, music and drama. I always get my homework in on time. I suppose, really, I like the work we do in school.

WISE OLD
OWL: *(thinking again)* Hmm. Hmm. And are you prepared to change to stop this happening?

PETER: No. I've thought about it, but I like doing the things I do and being the way I am.

WISE OLD
OWL: Hmm. Good. Good. *(Pause)* It's been a difficult day for you, hasn't it?

PETER: Very.

WISE OLD
OWL: Well, I'm not going to make it much easier for you, I'm afraid. There are no easy answers to this problem, and any solution is up to you. You see, all the animals you spoke to were right.

PETER: All of them? What do you mean?

WISE OLD
OWL: Well, you see, the rabbits were right in one way. If you can avoid getting into a situation where the bullies can get at you, that would be a sensible sort of running away.

Photocopiable

PETER: Yes, I can see that. But what about the rats?

WISE OLD OWL: Well, you already irritate the bullies, don't you, by deciding to carry on being different? If you keep doing the things you like best and being who you want to be, maybe they will get tired of trying to change you.

PETER: *(beginning to get excited)* Yes, that might work! But how can the wolves be right? I can't possibly fight back.

WISE OLD OWL: Hmm. Hmm. Yes you can, Peter. Here's how. Remember what the other animals said?

PETER: Well the birds said I should tell everyone and the foxes said I should be sly and cunning.

WISE OLD OWL: Exactly! So this is what you must do, Peter. Do as the birds say and tell everyone. Tell your parents, the teachers, lunchtime organisers… everyone… every time the bullies start picking on you. Once everyone knows who they are and what they are doing, your problem will be shared.

PETER: So how can I be sly and cunning?

WISE OLD OWL: Hmm. Hmm. This is a much more difficult part of the answer, I'm afraid, Peter, and one that needs just as much courage as the others. We know you are bullied because you are different from them, so you need to try and understand just how they feel. Why do you think they take your homework?

PETER: *(considering)* Maybe it's because they never get their own homework done.

WISE OLD OWL: So, *(Pause)* is there anything you can do about that?

Photocopiable

PETER: *(thinking carefully)* Well, maybe I could help them, if they would like.

WISE OLD
OWL: Perfect! Well, Peter, the day will soon be over. Time for me to get out and about, hunting and hooting.

PETER: Thanks, Mr Owl. You really are the wisest creature in the forest. Please thank all the other animals for me, too. Tomorrow I will start my fight back – with their help.

PETER exits.
The lights fade to blackout and the WISE OLD OWL exits, removing the chair.

SCENE 9: School, a few days later

The CHILDREN are all sitting in front of MRS MOORE.

MRS MOORE: This is excellent! Homework in from everybody for the first time. Well done, class! I'm happy to say that no one will be kept in today, so off you all go.

The CHILDREN all exit. MRS MOORE also exits, smiling happily.
The CHILDREN all enter again.

TOMMY: Thanks, Peter. My dad was really chuffed when I showed him I could do long division.

LUCY: I think that's the first time Mrs Moore's been nice to me.

CLAIRE: And me!

SALLY: It's nice being able to hand homework in, isn't it?

BILLY: *(shrugging uncertainly)* It's all right.

LENNY: *(hesitating)* Er… we're going for a game of football, Peter, you coming?

PETER: Well…

FRANKIE: Oh, leave him. He doesn't want to play with us.

PETER: Well, I'll keep goal for a bit if you like.

LENNY: OK. Have we got goalposts?

TOMMY: I'm not allowed to use my jumper again – it's still got mud on it from last time!

PETER: We can use my coat if you like.

FRANKIE: Great! Come on, then. Me and Billy will be Man City, *(To LENNY)* you and Tommy can be Man United.

LENNY: I don't want to be United, we were United last time!

FRANKIE: You'd better be United or I'll make you be Chester!

The CHILDREN exit except PETER.

PETER: *(to the audience)* I suppose all the animals were right in a way. There are lots of different ways of dealing with bullies and no simple answers. *(He nods towards where the others have just exited)* They will probably still bully others, but at least they're not bullying me. You have to do what's right for you when other people are picking on you, but it's important for everyone to find their own wise old owl and listen to his good advice – just like I did.

PETER exits, following the other CHILDREN.
The lights fade to blackout. The curtains close.

THE END

PRODUCTION SUPPORT

AUDITIONS AND CASTING

The easiest way to begin the audition process is to read through the play with the children two or three times. The initial reading should simply be an exercise in familiarising them with the material. The second read-through should enable children to volunteer to read specific character parts, and the third should be used for you to nominate specific children to read certain character parts. During the second and third readings, encourage the children to think about using vocal expression, following the stage directions and picking up their cues quickly. Write yourself notes about how the children perform when reading specific roles. At every read-through, you must give each child a chance to read something.

It is important to make a concerted effort to allow less confident readers a chance to read, encouraging others in the group to show patience and consideration when listening. Plays always help poor readers to develop their language skills, and their enthusiasm in wanting to perform often leads to a great deal of work away from the rehearsals to ensure that they know their lines. A poor reader does not necessarily make a poor actor.

There are several alternative methods for casting your play and the process can be as formal or informal as you wish.

FORMAL AUDITIONS
These can be held by selecting specific speeches or scenes from the play and asking the children to learn and recite them, or read them through, in various group combinations. The drawback of this method is that it takes an inordinate amount of time to plan and execute, and can make children very tense and often unable to perform well, especially if their memory skills are not strong.

CHILDREN CHOOSING THEIR OWN ROLES
Another option is to ask the children to write their first and second role choices, confidentially, on pieces of paper. Ask them to try to make sure the spelling is correct and to add their full names. Some children will only have one choice of role, others will all go for the same first choice and there will be some children who 'don't care' what role they are given!

Gather all the pieces of paper together and, in a quiet place at another time, sit down and work out who wants what and which role combinations would work. Try to be as fair as possible, both to the children and to the play. Children are often aware of their 'failings' as actors and usually accept that others have stronger performance skills, but this doesn't prevent many children from feeling acute disappointment if they fail to secure the role they are desperate for.

When allocating roles after using this method, ask the children to sit in a circle and read from the bottom of the cast list upwards, giving the name of the character first and then the name of the child who has been given that part. Sometimes a little of what is known as 'director speak' (see page 46) may be useful for convincing upset children that they are more suited to smaller 'character' roles than to a main part.

After each part has been allocated, allow the children up to 5 minutes to discuss the casting and to accept and compare their roles.

DRAWING NAMES OUT OF A HAT
Another method which is fairer, but far more risky for your play, is to ask the children to put their names into a hat and to draw a name for each character. Children have mixed feelings about this process: there is always a possibility that their name will be drawn for the character they want to play, but they know that this is not guaranteed. Also, less confident children occasionally end up with large roles which they really don't feel happy or comfortable about performing.

CHOOSING ACTORS YOURSELF
The final option is simply to allocate the roles yourself, choosing children who you know are able and confident. However, this can upset other children who are rarely given the opportunity to perform, and removes any sense of the children being involved in the casting process.

After a number of years and a number of arguments, floods of tears and several very unhappy children, I have reached the conclusion that the second method – children choosing their own roles – is the fairest and surest option. It gives children a chance to specify which roles they would like to perform, and gives you the opportunity to make the final decision in a

Peter's Problem

considered manner. It always surprises me which parts children choose to go for, and which appear to be the most popular! Sometimes children who appear confident – and who might have otherwise been given a major role – select small parts; likewise, children who appear less confident choose more demanding roles.

It is not strictly necessary to cast according to gender. Give females the opportunity to play male roles, and vice versa. The children will enjoy having the option of selecting a role because of what it is, without being restricted to their own gender.

I feel strongly that children's enthusiasm for playing their particular parts will result in an eagerness to learn lines, a willingness to throw themselves into the roles wholeheartedly and an easier rehearsal process. I have been vindicated in this belief over and over again when 'risking' a major part on a child who may not have been given a chance to shine had I chosen a different casting method.

Whichever casting method you choose, once the roles have been allocated you should then ask the children to sit in a circle, arranging them according to character or family groups. Read through the play again together, to get the feel of how it sounds with all the roles established.

Finally, tell the children that each person in the cast is as important as the next – without one character, you don't have a full team and, therefore, a complete play. They won't believe you – they've already spent time counting the number of lines they have to say – but it *is* true and needs to be expressed.

DIRECTOR SPEAK

Whatever decisions you make about casting, and however fair you try to be, there may be children who are upset when the parts are distributed. Many children feel that they never have the opportunity to show what they can do; some can build up quite a strong resentment against others who always seem to get the main roles; and quieter children can feel a sense of failure at not having pushed themselves forward yet again.

These feelings need to be dealt with as sensitively and as quickly as possible, away from the main group. In these situations you must employ what is known as 'director speak' in an attempt to pacify, boost and reassure the children. This means using a variety of statements aimed to placate, such as:

- *I know you're upset about not getting the part you wanted, but I really needed a good actor for that scene to encourage all the others to perform well.*
- *I understand that you wanted a main part, but you read this part so well that I just had to give it to you.*
- *I appreciate that you're disappointed, but I wanted to give you the chance to try something different this time, to show me what you can do.*
- *I realise you might be a bit disappointed, but this character is very different from your own and will be a challenge for you, which I think you're ready for.*
- *I know that you're unhappy, but can you understand that I have to be fair to everyone and give others a chance to try a bigger part sometimes?*

And others of a similar nature. The children will probably recognise that you are trying to pacify them, but what is important about using 'director speak' is that you are hearing and acknowledging their feelings of unhappiness and that they have had the opportunity to express these feelings.

Whatever you say is not going to make a lot of difference to some children. In these cases, they need to be given a direct choice between playing the part they have been given and not being in the play at all – however cruel that may seem. Most children will choose the former option. Any child opting out of the play should be kept occupied with other tasks, such as painting scenery, prompting, or making props and costumes. They will often regret their decision to pull out and, if possible, should be given the chance to join in again.

The main issue in the production of a play that is likely to anger and upset children is the feeling of a sense of unfairness about the part allocation. Therefore if, when using 'director speak' on a previous occasion, you have promised a bigger part to a child next time, you must keep your promise! Also, if you have stated that 'everyone needs to be given a chance', then do not allocate the main roles to the same children as were chosen last time.

Remember that all actors have fragile egos and child actors are no exception. In selecting or auditioning for a role they are putting themselves firmly in the firing line, exposing their wishes and asking you to praise their abilities, while all the time anticipating that they will be shot down. The worst thing you can do is to negate these feelings and ignore their insecurities. Even as an adult actor, I have felt upset at not being given a part I desperately wanted, and those feelings can be magnified a hundred times for children.

Don't use 'director speak' simply to make life easier for yourself, though it can help to create a positive working environment. I use it all the time, and try to be reasonable, fair and understanding in the way I use it. In that context it works.

STRUCTURING REHEARSALS

When faced with directing a play, it is sometimes difficult to know what to tackle first. You have a large group of children awaiting your instructions, a limited amount of access to the school hall and very little time! Good pre-rehearsal planning and preparation is therefore essential. The following timetable may be useful.

PREPARATION

Immediately after casting, spend an hour or two resolving practicalities: what sort of stage the play will be performed on; how many entrances and exits you will have, and where these will be (plus a consideration of the imaginary setting that lies beyond them, if relevant); where the children will go when they are not on stage; exactly how and where each character enters and exits; what scenery, furniture and props you will have (if any), and where these will be positioned on the stage; whether any characters will enter from other parts of the auditorium and, if so, where from. All these points need to be clearly defined to your own satisfaction before starting rehearsals.

REHEARSALS 1 TO 3

These should be used to complete what is known as 'blocking' – simply specifying the movements of the children on, off and around the stage. Explain your staging ideas to the cast, marking out the stage area and exits with chairs. Tell the children what furniture and scenery will be on stage, and use chairs or other equipment to represent this as well. Take time to ensure that all of the cast are familiar with the setting, the acting arena and their movements before continuing. They'll be desperate to get on with the 'acting', but it is essential that they understand the space they are working in and know their moves before going any further. It is impossible to teach children to act and give them instructions about where to enter and exit at the same time.

REHEARSALS 4 TO 8

Break the play down into small sections and rehearse these individually. Don't try to work through the whole play in one rehearsal at this point. Start from the beginning and work through up to three scenes. Rehearse the same section a number of times, until you feel that familiarity is beginning to reduce the children's interest, then move on to the next section.

Continue the following rehearsal from where you left off the last time; never repeat the previous section and then move on, or the result will be one or two sections that are brilliant and a number that are completely under-rehearsed. This will mean that some of the children are unoccupied for some of the rehearsals. They can use their time productively by learning their lines in pairs, watching the play and making notes, giving you feedback about how it looks, making props, designing posters and programmes, and so on. Insist that they remain aware of what is going on – they could be called to rehearsal at any time!

Carry on rehearsing the play in small sections until you have completed the whole script. Make notes as you go along of any potential difficulties, any scenes or characters which you feel will need extra rehearsing and any ideas that you have for scenery, props, costumes or effects.

REHEARSALS 9 TO 11

Use these rehearsals to concentrate on scenes or sections that need extra attention. Try to get through the whole play at least once during each rehearsal period, but don't worry if you fail to do so! Again, never go back over sections; always start the next rehearsal from the point at which you finished the last one.

REHEARSALS 12 TO 14

Used for complete run-throughs, these should comprise a technical rehearsal (to practise using any lights, sound, props, music or special effects you might be including) and two dress rehearsals complete with costumes and make-up. Spend 10 minutes at the beginning of the final dress rehearsal to work out and practise your 'curtain call', then run through the play completely without stopping.

Final rehearsals are always a nightmare: the children are stressed and excited, you're stressed and beginning to panic, and everyone seems to be snapping at each other! Try to keep the children occupied at all times. Plan what you want to achieve in the rehearsals and try to stick to your plan.

I appreciate that this is the rehearsal structure for the 'ideal world' and it doesn't take into account those little things sent to try us: children being absent, falling out, not learning their lines, forgetting everything they learned during the last rehearsal, the props and costumes failing to materialise… But those stresses are what give us the sense of achievement when the play finally goes on – and it does always go on, despite the horrendous feeling that it will fail. The old saying 'It'll be all right on the night' usually applies!

STAGING AND SCENERY

Peter's Problem can be very simple to stage. It was first performed on a 'proscenium arch' stage (a square, raised stage that resembles a box, with structured spaces at the side for 'wings' and full curtains). There was no set – the stage was completely bare and the children acted against a simple background of black curtains. Any props or furniture used were brought on and removed by the actors. The only drawback of performing on a bare stage is that the children need to work a little bit harder in their acting to establish settings and create atmospheres.

The majority of the characters simply walked on from the wings at the side of the stage to make their entrances, and exited in the same manner. All the sections of the stage were used to good effect. The children used the whole of the stage area in the first scene, ending with the dialogue between PETER and SALLY being played at the front of the stage. The classroom was set on one half of the stage, allowing the children to re-enter on the other side of the stage for the following scene. The forest scenes (4 to 8) alternated between one half of the stage and the other, providing clarity and variation, and allowing the actors time and space to enter and exit.

Furniture was kept to a minimum. We didn't use chairs or desks for the classroom scene – the actors playing the children sat on the floor, with the teacher in front of them. This scene is so short, it is not worth creating an elaborate set, and the simple allusion to a classroom in the positioning of the actors was sufficient. The only items used were a tree stump, which was set and then removed, and a rocking chair for the WISE OLD OWL, who brought it on and took it off with him.

Our audience accepted the different settings in the play without the need for elaborate scenery, proving that the play can be successful if performed simply against black curtains.

The essential consideration if staging it in this manner is *pace*. Keep the entrances and exits swift, blending them as much as possible – at the same time that a character is leaving in one direction, a different character should be entering from another.

Similarly, work hard to ensure that the scenes do not become too static. Scene 7 retains the action in one place for a long time and some creative movement is required to ensure that audiences do not become bored by the lack of change. Also, remember that actors do not necessarily have to restrict their entrances and exits to the stage area alone. You can create good effects by using other areas of the hall, and this can create an interesting diversion for your audience.

This should all provide enough variety to keep the audience interested without your having to resort to creating elaborate scene changes. However, if you want to be more adventurous and use scenery, there are a number of options open to you.

If the children are performing on a proscenium arch stage, the solid back wall (known as the cyclorama or cyc) can be decorated with fixed scenery that will be appropriate for most of the scenes in the play, or that presents a general theme. The scenery could be a 'brick wall' pattern, to illustrate buildings, or trees and flowers, which could be used to decorate both the cyclorama and/or the proscenium arches.

Alternatively, you could take the 'general theme' idea one step further for this play by decorating your stage with appropriate animal and woodland images and these motifs could then be left as a permanent part of the scenery throughout the play. Any of these ideas would provide fixed scenery suitable for the majority of the scenes.

Any scenery effects for decorating your stage can be painted onto large sheets of lining paper or fabric, and fixed to the proscenium arches to avoid leaving permanent marks. A similar process would work for the scenery attached to the cyclorama. Just make sure that whatever you use to attach the scenery holds it on well!

If you perform plays on simple raised rostra, as in many schools, you could create simple wooden or cardboard screens to act as wings (on either side of the stage) and a back wall. You could decorate these with the general theme motifs as well as brickwork patterns, or trees and flowers. Room dividers, or similar, are useful for this. Again, these can remain in place throughout the play, acting as a permanent backdrop for all of the scenes.

If, however, you would like to change the scenery for each new setting, you will obviously require some form of changeable backdrop. If you have a pulley system at your school, you can use this to hang painted backdrops. However, you are limited to the number of backdrops you can fit on a pulley system, and so this method is not ideal. Other options include:

● Painting scenery onto large sheets of fabric and draping these over a long clothes rail (the type you find in warehouses or large stores). The rail can be swung round on castors to show the reverse side of any painted cloth, providing an instant scene change.

● Painting scenery onto large wooden or cardboard screens with castors attached, and wheeling these on to provide a movable backdrop.

● Asking any would-be carpenters to make a large wooden frame, approximately 8' × 6'. Attach a large piece of muslin or cotton to it firmly, then stretch the fabric tightly across and around the edge of the frame. Fix castors to the bottom and paint your scenery design onto it. This can then be wheeled on to provide an instant backdrop. Fabric could be attached to both sides of the frame, providing two backdrops. The main problem then is getting the large screens on and off the stage, and storing them when they are not in use!

● Fixing a long, detachable pole across the back of the stage area and attaching several pieces of fabric, with a different scene painted on each one, in a 'flip chart' arrangement. The backdrops can then be flipped over at appropriate points.

● Using the same detachable pole, but drawing the fabric, like curtains, across the back of the stage area. This will only provide one scenery change, however.

● If you are performing on a proscenium arch stage and have curtains at the back, these can be closed over any scenery painted on the cyclorama during subsequent scenes to provide an instant change. It is essential, though, that someone remembers to open them again if you have to return to your original setting.

Whatever you choose, it is important to remember two things:

● It is no great shame to select fixed scenery as an option. It is much better to spend what limited time and resources you have in creating a wonderfully elaborate setting that remains fixed, than to fail in trying to create a large variety of different scenery effects.

● Movable scenery means that someone has to be responsible for bringing it on and taking it off at the right moments, and that you have to find somewhere for it to be stored when not in use. The same rule applies to any changeable scenery. It has to be changed by someone, who also has to remember to change it back again if required.

If your actors have to bring on and remove any scenery, furniture or props, ensure that everyone is clear about what they are responsible for, and make sure that you rehearse scene changes as many times as you can. Audiences will forgive most things, but lengthy scene changes always cause them a great deal of irritation!

LIGHTING

Lighting in a play should be used to establish time, enhance setting or create atmosphere. If you are lucky enough to have a professional theatre lighting rig, you can create some wonderful lighting effects. If not, simple lighting can often be sufficient to establish the basics.

Our production of *Peter's Problem* was lit very simply with what is known as a 'general wash' for the majority of the play – the stage was flooded with light. The action in the play takes place over a short period of time, reducing the need for elaborate time changes and allowing the lighting to remain fairly constant throughout the play.

If you have the facility to dim or increase your lights, use this to good effect, especially to illustrate the atmospheres in the different areas of the forest, or to create a homely effect inside the WISE OLD OWL's elm tree. If you do not have the facilities to change any lights at all, simply leave them on full for the whole play, as this will not hinder the audience's appreciation of the performance. An alternative option would be to borrow or hire some free-standing lights which could be positioned at the side of your stage and used to create a spooky effect for the forest scenes.

If you have a professional lighting rig, you could use coloured 'gels' to create atmospheric lighting effects. These are transparencies which fit over spotlights to give them a coloured glow. They must be heat-resistant and should only be purchased from a theatre lighting specialist. A couple of spotlights with green and blue gels attached, combined with standard (clear white) spots, will give an excellent gloomy setting for the forest, particularly for the entrance of the WOLVES, and could be used again to indicate PETER's despondent mood during his visit to the

WISE OLD OWL. The change in his mood to one of optimism could then be indicated by using a mixture of red and yellow gels in place of the blue ones.

We were fortunate enough to have access to professional spotlights for our production, but still kept the lighting effects very simple. For most of the scenes the stage was simply flooded with light – not subtle, but effective. Blackouts (extinguishing all lights) were used occasionally to close a scene and in preparation for the curtain call. For a stage with no front curtains, blackouts can be useful, but make sure that your actors and crew have practised moving around in the dark!

MUSIC AND SOUND EFFECTS

The only music we used in our production of *Peter's Problem* was a well-known pop song sung by the BIRDS in Scene 7. We selected a song by The Spice Girls (karaoke tapes of their songs are available from a number of shops) and the children practised and sang a short extract. Although we did not use any pre-recorded music, it could be used effectively to create atmosphere and set the scene. Choose any songs or musical pieces which reflect the themes of bullying and animals, or which highlight the magical aspect of the play. Select one to use at the beginning and end of the play. This will then act as a 'curtain', signalling to the audience when the play is starting and finishing. (Before using music in a public performance, check that your school has the relevant broadcast licences.)

Other musical extracts or songs could be used in various ways during the play:

- Songs associated with playground games could be included in Scene 1.
- PETER could sing a solo at the end of Scene 3 to indicate his feelings of sadness and loneliness. This could be repeated at specific points during the play, particularly at the end of Scenes 5 and 6.
- The RABBITS could sing about playing and having fun before PETER's entrance in Scene 4.
- Other animals could be introduced by songs or music, especially the RATS, BIRDS and WOLVES, but the entrance of the FOXES may be difficult to accompany with a song as they arrive half-way through the scene.
- Spooky, haunting instrumental music could be used to introduce, or underscore the entrances of, some of the animals. This would work particularly well with the WOLVES and FOXES.

- A short extract from Prokofiev's *Peter and the Wolf* could be used as background music when PETER meets the WOLF 1 in Scene 6.
- The WISE OLD OWL could sing a solo before PETER's entrance in Scene 8. This could focus on his intelligence or refer to how happy he is living in his tree.
- A song demonstrating PETER's happier mood could be included after his discussion with the WISE OLD OWL at the end of Scene 8.
- An upbeat finale song, with the whole cast back on stage, could be included at the end of the play.

I don't recommend that any other incidental music is used during the play, though it could be interesting to use music as a character theme by playing the same tune each time a specific character enters. This could work well with both the bullies and the different animals, but it should only really be attempted with one or two characters, and its use limited to avoid irritating the audience.

However, if you want to include more music in your production of *Peter's Problem*, make your selections carefully. If you have the time, try to search for musical extracts that reflect specific characters' moods or emphasise the play's themes.

Alternatively, you could use music lessons in school for the children to compose original music or songs for the play that reflect the characters and settings. If you choose to include songs and do not want your actors to sing, other children in the school can be employed as a chorus. They can be seated around the stage area, singing the songs while those on stage mime appropriate actions.

Also, don't forget to utilise your talented school musicians – both teachers and pupils! The music doesn't have to be tuneful or played from musical scores. Interesting musical sound effects can be created with a variety of unusual or home-made instruments. My big moment (as a teacher) in a school production was providing the 'elephant' sounds on a baritone horn for a performance of *The Jungle Book*!

PROPS

Again, this play is simple to stage. The only props (an abbreviation of 'properties') that could be included are:

- school-bags for the children in Scenes 1 to 3
- PETER'S homework book in Scene 1
- appropriate items for the bullies to tip out of PETER's bag in Scene 1

- a tree stump for Scenes 4 and 7
- small boxes and bits of cardboard for the rats to move about in Scene 5
- a rocking chair for the WISE OLD OWL in Scene 8
- a pair of glasses, a reading book or puzzle book and pen for the WISE OLD OWL in Scene 8
- a football for Scene 9
- a coat for PETER in Scene 9.

Few of these are essential, however, and many of them could be omitted or mimed. The list above consists of all the props that we used, and they were quite sufficient.

The school-bags we used were quite small and the items in PETER's bag were restricted to a couple of books and a pencil case. This ensured that loose items didn't roll away when the bag was emptied.

The RATS were given pieces of cardboard, twigs and boxes to transfer across the stage, but these items could easily be mimed if you are concerned they might cause problems.

The WISE OLD OWL's glasses were just frames made from wire, without glass. This looks effective and prevents stage lights from reflecting oddly on the glass.

You could also use free-standing trees for the forest scenes and an additional chair in the WISE OLD OWL's tree, but be careful not to overcrowd the stage as too much furniture is a distraction to your actors and the audience.

If the actors react appropriately to any props used on stage, then the audience will believe what they see. Also, the distance between stage and audience always manages to create believable illusions – so technical perfection is rarely required.

The essential point to remember with all props and furniture is: 'If it goes on, it must come off.' If an item makes its way onto the stage, then it must somehow make its way off again! Actors (of all ages) are notoriously bad at remembering this!

COSTUMES

The costumes for *Peter's Problem* are also very simple. If, you have the time, resources and skill to create elaborate costumes, then feel free to do so! If not, the following ideas worked perfectly well for our production:

Peter and the other **children** all came from different schools, so using a uniform was difficult. They were, therefore, dressed in smart black trousers or skirts with white school shirts, plus smart black shoes. If you do have a school uniform, this would be preferable.

Mrs Moore wore a smart dress with smart shoes and a short cardigan.

Rabbits were dressed in white or brown leotards. We sewed white pompons on the bottom of their leotards and gripped floppy ears made of felt into their hair. They had bare legs and feet.

Rats were dressed in black, brown or grey leotards with corresponding footless tights. Their tails were made by cutting pairs of tights in half and stuffing the individual legs with rolled-up bubble wrap; these were then pinned to the costumes using the spare flap of tights fabric. Small ears were made using stiff black and brown card and were either gripped directly into the children's hair, or onto dark headbands that they wore. They had bare feet which we covered with make-up in appropriate colours.

Wolves were dressed in black leggings and black sweatshirts. We bought black 'hairy' material that we rolled and sewed to make tails which were then pinned to the children's leggings. Long ears were made from stiff cardboard covered with felt and were gripped into the children's hair or onto headbands. The actors had bare feet which we covered with black make-up.

Birds were dressed in brightly-coloured leggings and T-shirts. We cut wings out of brightly-coloured fabric and these were pinned to the T-shirt at the base of the neck and strapped with elastic onto the children's wrists. Their beaks were half-cones of appropriately coloured card held on with very thin, flesh-coloured elastic around the head. We chose to only have half-cones to enable the actors to be heard! They had bare feet.

Foxes were dressed in brown leggings and brown jumpers. The tails were made from orange-brown crêpe paper cut into thin (approximately 1" wide) strips tied together at one end. They looked very bushy and were effective when the tied end was pinned to their leggings. Their ears were made from brown card covered in brown felt and either gripped into the hair, or fixed to a headband which they wore. They had bare feet which were covered in brown make-up.

Daffodils wore green leggings, or footless tights, and yellow T-shirts. We cut large yellow petals out of card, fixed these to another strip of yellow card as a backing and then fixed that (using glue) to cheap plastic headbands that the children wore as normal. You can use headbands that tone in with the children's hair colour or bright yellow ones that tone in with the petals. The children had bare feet.

Wise Old Owl wore brown leggings with a brown long-sleeved T-shirt. We then cut strips of darker brown, black and cream material into 'feather' shapes and sewed these onto the front, back and arms of the T-shirt. Small ears were made from brown and cream felt and gripped into the actor's hair. The child had bare feet which were covered with black make-up.

All animal ears were secured by creating a small extra flap of card or thick material at the bottom of each ear. This flap could then be either gripped directly into the hair, or gripped underneath an elasticated or hard plastic headband. Use plenty of grips and make

sure they're hair-coloured, not fashion grips! Which method you use will depend on the length and thickness of the child's hair.

If you want to make pointed noses for any of your animals, form cones out of black card fixed with strong glue and adhesive tape. Thread thin elastic through small holes at the side and measure this to go around the back of the child's head. Make your measurements carefully – both for the size of the noses and the length of the elastic!

Whiskers can be made from paint brush bristles stuck on with strong glue.

Most of the costumes we used were found in parents' wardrobes, children's own 'dressing-up' boxes or purchased from local charity shops. If you can't find heeled shoes to fit your female characters, then ballet pumps or tap shoes would work well. (It is advisable to remove the 'taps' for the play!) Black plimsolls are also very useful as a replacement for 'smart' shoes.

Do try to spend some time wandering around your local charity shops, and visiting local jumble sales. Many of the clothes that other people throw away make ideal costumes, or can easily be adapted, and cost very little. Some charity shops also sell offcuts of material very cheaply which can be cut up for decoration.

MAKE-UP

All make-up is dependent on the type of lighting used in your performance arena. If you are working under professional stage lights, then more must be applied, since these lights remove colour and contour from the face. However, if you are working under school lights or strip lights, be careful just to define features and express the characters.

Water-based make-up is excellent for whole face or body coverage; grease-based make-up is best for eyes, cheeks and lips. Both types of make-up can be purchased from any good theatrical costumier's, and many specialist companies provide a large variety of water-based face paints and theatre make-up. Practise applying make-up before the performances!

The make-up for *Peter's Problem* is fairly simple, although considerable practice in applying it is recommended! The following were used in our production (in which we worked under professional stage lights):

All the children were given a light base of foundation, simple, light lipstick, blue eyeshadow and a little brick-red blusher. We also defined their eyes by using a thin line of black eyeliner next to the top and bottom eyelashes. Try to prevent the children from applying too much make-up. It is more important that they look as natural as possible without losing facial contours.

Mrs Moore was given a light base, blue eyeshadow, a darker red blusher and bright red or pink lipstick.

Rabbits were given pink-toned bases, darker pink eyes, black noses created with a grease stick and whiskers drawn on with a black eyeliner pencil. We also 'blanked out' their own lips using the foundation base and painted on large white teeth, outlined very thinly in black to define them.

Rats were given a slightly darker foundation base with black eyeshadow, black noses, whiskers and teeth.

Wolves were given a dark base combined with dark brown or purple lips, dark brown or purple eyeshadow and whiskers.

Birds had coloured bases in green, yellow or blue. We painted their eyelids in bright, contrasting colours and extended the make-up line away from the eyes to give them an exotic, oriental look. We used orange, purple and red to colour their lips and defined their eyes using a thin line of black eyeliner.

Foxes were given a brown base combined with lighter brown eyeshadow. We defined their eyes using black eyeliner and this was extended outwards to make the eyes seem longer and narrower. A black grease stick was used to create a black nose and a black eyeliner pencil to draw on whiskers.

Daffodils had yellow bases that completely covered their faces and lips. Combined with this, we used a white grease stick on and around their eyes.

Wise Old Owl was given a light-brown base. We used a black grease stick for eyeshadow, applied both over and underneath the eyes. We also applied black greasepaint to the lips.

The coloured bases we used were water-based and so quick and easy to apply to large areas of flesh. Ordinary face paints are ideal. The main aspect of making-up children for *Peter's Problem* is to be aware of the enormous amount of time it takes! If possible (and it is highly recommended) recruit some parents or older pupils to assist.

Make-up is part of theatre that children love. It makes them aware of the different and magical world they are involved in. Following are some application hints and other ideas for effects.

If you want to 'age' your actors, use a red-toned grease stick and a cocktail stick. Ask the children to screw up their faces and apply the greasepaint to the wrinkles with the cocktail stick. Think carefully about where wrinkles form on the face as you age and simply draw them in. Be careful not to put in too many lines, though, or the poor child will end up with a face like a road map!

If you want to give any of your characters a real moustache, fake hair can be purchased for this purpose. It comes in small plaits or strips and needs teasing into shape. You then fix it to the face using spirit gum, which should hold it on firmly throughout the performance.

Any base or foundation should be applied all over the face and neck area, including the ears and the back of the neck. A small amount of make-up must also be used to cover any other areas of bare flesh, such as arms and hands. For large expanses of skin, water-based make-up is quickest and most effective. It is important to cover all 'bare flesh' areas, especially if working under professional theatre lighting, as the lights will show very clearly the distinction between made-up and non-made-up flesh.

Water-based cake make-up, or face paint, needs to be applied with a sponge that is barely damp and fully covered with make-up. If you have too much water on your sponge, the make-up will streak and application will be patchy. If you decide to use grease sticks to create a base or foundation, select a brick red and a colour slightly paler than the child's skin. Apply the pale colour all over the face first, blending well with your fingers, and then dot the red on forehead, cheeks, chin and nose, and blend it in thoroughly and carefully. The face should then have a good foundation base on which you can apply other colours. If not, keep adding more of either colour and blending thoroughly until you are happy with the result. Use the same technique for all other areas of bare skin.

'Set' any grease make-up with a light dusting of loose powder to keep in it place under the hot stage lights. Take care when applying blusher using a grease stick – a little goes a very long way. Grease sticks for eyeshadow come in a variety of colours (not just blue), and any of these can be used to make up your characters. It is a superstition, though, that green eyeshadow is *never* worn in the theatre – you have been warned!

Try to avoid using ordinary make-up for the stage. It is not suitable and rarely withstands the heat, often fading within a few moments of being applied. Theatre make-up is specifically designed for the stage and it is worth spending £20 or £30 on purchasing a good selection of proper theatrical make-up.

Other items that would be useful for your make-up box include: hair gel, talcum powder (for whitening hair), fake blood (mix glycerine with red food colouring), a stipple brush (or small blusher brush) used with a black grease stick for creating facial stubble, fake hair and spirit gum for applying it, cocktail sticks for creating age lines, teeth blackout liquid, coloured hairspray, glitter gels and a variety of coloured grease sticks.

LEARNING LINES

Children never fail to amaze me with their capacity for learning and retaining lines. However, everyone needs support in learning lines at some time and these are some of the methods that can help:

REPETITION

This requires constant and regular reading of the script. Go over the children's lines again and again, and they will learn them by rote. Using this method means that children often learn everyone else's lines as well, which is not a problem unless they insist on prompting while on stage!

FROM CUES

Read the line immediately before theirs. Let the child read their line out loud. Read the 'cue line' again, but this time cover up the child's line on the script. This way, the children are learning the important cues as well as their own lines.

ON PAPER

Write the cue lines and their own lines on a separate piece of paper, to prevent them being daunted by a large script. Use this method for children to learn one scene or short section at a time. They can carry the piece of paper around with them wherever they go, and will memorise the lines quite quickly by absorbing these short extracts.

ON TAPE

Help the children to read through the script two or three times. Record their cue lines on tape, leaving a long pause after each one for them to interject with their own lines. Work through this with them initially, using the script as an accompanying visual aid, then let them try it alone. Gradually remove their dependence on using the script, until they can say their lines in the pauses on the tape without hesitating. Alternatively, record cue lines and their lines and then leave a gap for them to repeat their own lines.

VERBAL SUPPORT

Some children find it easier to learn lines through hearing them spoken and simply repeating them. However, this can take up an awful lot of your rehearsal time! Enlist the support of family members and carers to help the children with their lines. Encourage the children to 'test' each other and try to create an atmosphere of support. Don't be too worried if children paraphrase their lines, so long as important aspects of the script are not omitted.

IN A WHOLE GROUP

Use what literacy time you can to read through the script a number of times as a whole group. Try to balance the need for the children to remember what they have to say with not frightening them so much that they forget everything!

Children should, however, be made aware of the fact that they will not be able to take their scripts (or pieces of paper) onto the stage with them. This should be made clear as early in the rehearsal process as possible, to ensure that they all understand.

The most secure approach is to ensure that the children know and, if possible, learn the whole script. This builds their knowledge of what should happen in each scene, and means that the children can improvise or say another character's lines if something goes wrong.

LINE-LEARNING REHEARSALS

If you have the time, include in your rehearsal schedule one or two line-learning sessions. Sit with the children in a circle, positioning them in character order, and tell them to recite the whole play without looking at their scripts (these should be placed face down on the floor in front of them). This can be helpful for the person who is prompting as well. It will also make you aware of which children need more help with learning their lines.

PROMPTERS

Prompters should only give the first word of a sentence, then supply more words if the actor is still struggling. Make sure that only one person is responsible for prompting, and give them every possible opportunity to practise their skill.

REHEARSALS WITHOUT SCRIPTS

It is a good idea to tell the children a specific day by which they must have learned all of their lines. Tell them which rehearsal this will be – and stick to it! At that rehearsal, don't allow any children to go on with